# Early Readers

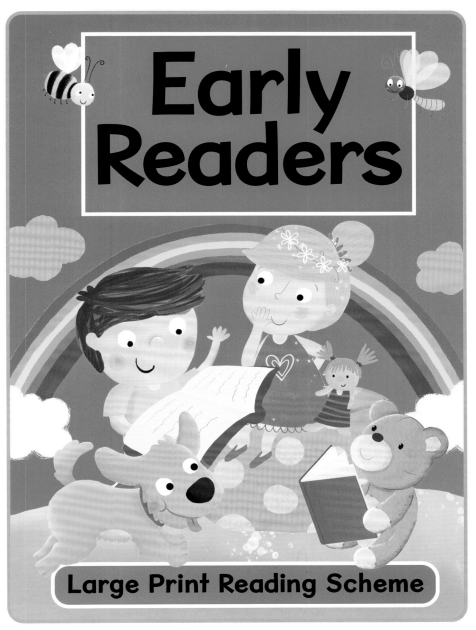

## Large Print Reading Scheme

Written by Gill Davies
Illustrated by Angelika Scudamore

**Brown Watson**

ENGLAND

First Published 2016 by Brown Watson
The Old Mill, 76 Fleckney Road, Kibworth Beauchamp
Leicestershire, LE8 0HG

ISBN: 978 0 7097 2319 6

# A LONG WALK HOME

The three children are very tired. They have been out shopping all day and are now too tired to walk anymore.

'I wish we were grown up and had one car each like the ones over there,' sighed Paul. 'Then we could race home.'

'Racing is not very safe,' says Dad. 'Just keep walking. We shall be home soon.'

'I wish there was a whale, waiting to race us through the sea right up to the beach and our house on the hill,' sighs James.

'You'd still have to climb the hill,' says Mum. 'And then you'd be even more tired. Keep walking. We shall be home soon.'

'I wish we had a magic carpet,' sighs Jenny...

'…Then we could fly in the sky faster than a car on the road or a whale in the sea.'

'Well,' says Dad, 'You have all been talking and dreaming so much you have not noticed that we have taken a short cut. Here we are – home at last.'

He opens the door and the happy children rush inside, suddenly awake again and ready to play.

# KEY WORDS

| | |
|---|---|
| all | shall |
| hill | fly |
| just | more |
| you | three |
| taken | right |
| faster | or |
| one | that |
| too | play |

# WHAT CAN YOU SEE HERE?

bunting

window

fishes

car

palm tree

# HOLLY AND POLLY

Holly and Polly were girl twins who always played together and loved dressing up as princesses.

'I don't like boys,' said Polly.
'Nor do I,' said Holly.
'Let's not ask any to our birthday party next week,' said Polly.

'Right,' agreed Holly.
'No horrid boys at all.
Not never ever!'

Holly and Polly were so busy giggling and running that they did not see the slippy, drippy mud. They did not see it at all and slipped right over. Down! Splat!

'Ha,' said Rabbit, hopping by. 'That serves you right. You were being horrid about boys. Some of them are really quite nice. I happen to be a boy rabbit, you know.'

Holly and Polly felt bad. They told Rabbit he was quite right. Boys were not that bad, really. They were being silly.

So they did ask a boy to their party, just one – their brother, Harry... Mummy said he had to come, anyway.

'We like your brother,' their friends giggled later, 'He is great fun, even if he is a boy.'

# KEY WORDS

| | |
|---|---|
| fun | down |
| girl | play |
| our | he |
| know | friends |
| who | ask |
| love | but |
| brother | did |
| to | very |

# WHAT CAN YOU SEE HERE?

bird

flower

butterfly

rabbit

juice

apples

17

# PIRATE PALS

'What do you want to be when you grow up?' Peter's uncle always asks him.

'A pirate,' he says, 'A pirate sailing over the sea.'

'Well, make sure you bring us back some treasure,' his uncle laughs. Then one night Pirate Percy jumps into Peter's bedroom, shouting, 'Come with me, lad.' Away they fly into the sky.

Soon they arrive at the ship. Pirates are singing, sleeping or pulling on ropes and sails. One young lad, Tom, scrubs the deck. He looks very tired so Peter helps him.

Then Tom shows Peter all over the ship. It is very exciting. There is even a cow to give them milk.

Peter, who is just admiring the cannon, asks, 'Can I possibly borrow some treasure to show my uncle please?'

All the pirates look worried but Percy says, 'Fine. You can bring it back next time.' He gives Peter two shiny gold pieces.

'Wow!' thinks Peter, 'Now I can't wait for my uncle to visit again!'

# KEY WORDS

| | |
|---|---|
| next | help |
| milk | give |
| sleeping | fly |
| into | for |
| bring | jumps |
| away | at |
| singing | so |
| thinks | with |

# WHAT CAN YOU SEE HERE?

moon

cannon balls

rat

window

pirate

book

25

# THE BIRTHDAY CAKE

Jenny likes to cook. She ties her hair back and puts on a tall white hat, just like a real cook. Today, while her younger sisters play, she makes a beautiful pink cake. Her eldest sister Kate arrives. She is a very good cook, too.

'The king is very sad,' Kate says. 'His cook is ill and he would like a cake for his birthday.'

'Why don't we make him one together?' says Kate.

So that is what they do. They make a really fine chocolate cake. But Jenny is worried. 'Oh dear!' she says. 'We have no candles. What can we do?'

'Let's make little sugar crowns instead,' says Kate … so that is what they do.

Kate and Jenny take the cake to the king 'Yummy!' he says. 'This is wonderful!'
The children sing 'Happy Birthday'. Then Jenny says, 'I am so sorry there are no candles.'

'But I am pleased,' laughs the king. 'Everyone in the palace wants a turn at blowing them out and then I have to wait to eat my cake. But today we can start munching straight away!'

# KEY WORDS

| | |
|---|---|
| about | here |
| dear | make |
| everyone | sisters |
| really | good |
| sad | be |
| friend | little |
| but | sad |
| again | needs |

# WHAT CAN YOU SEE HERE?

salad

sandwiches

puppy

cupcakes

cake

jars

# OSCAR HATES STORMS

Oscar the Octopus is afraid. He hates storms. He hates the loud thunder and the bright lights flashing in the sky. There is nowhere to go, no place to hide.

This is a very big bad storm – and it is getting worse … Bang! Bang! Flash! Flash!

'Oh dear,' sobs Oscar. 'Who will help me?'

Then Oscar spots a boat. He swims across the sea. He tries to get onto the boat. He wants to hide inside.

Sailor Sam does not know that Oscar is just scared. Sam is scared too. He is scared of the storm and he is scared of Oscar, so he pushes Oscar off the boat and then sails away fast.

At last, a brave sea knight gallops up. 'Come with me,' he says to Oscar. 'I can take you to a place where there are no storms. The sea is warm and there are lots of sea creatures who would love to be friends with you.'

How happy Oscar is as he follows the knight to his new home.

# KEY WORDS

| | |
|---|---|
| lots | you |
| very | would |
| sea | place |
| can | horses |
| bad | as |
| his | this |
| home | off |
| where | getting |

# WHAT CAN YOU SEE HERE?

octopus

crab

starfish

Sailor Sam

boat

barrels

# THREE BRAVE BROTHERS

'I don't believe in giants,' said George, 'Or big monsters!' He was quite sure that there were no such things …

But that was before he fell asleep and dreamed of a huge purple monster with three eyes and four sharp teeth.

George woke up, fell out of bed and ran into Mummy and Daddy's room.

George's brother, Henry, had said, 'I don't believe in fairies or dragons!' He was quite sure there were no such things...

But that was before he fell asleep and dreamed of a huge yellow dragon breathing hot fire.

Henry woke up, fell out of bed and ran into his parents' room. He squeezed in next to George.

'All dinosaurs died out long ago,' said Charlie. But when he fell asleep he dreamed that a huge orange dinosaur was grinning at him.

Charlie ran to his parents' room and squeezed in ...'This bed is getting very full,' sighed Daddy.

'Full of my adorable little monsters!' said Mummy, hugging all three boys until they fell fast asleep again.

# KEY WORDS

| | |
|---|---|
| again | three |
| into | four |
| big | bed |
| before | all |
| very | things |
| yellow | now |
| was | him |
| and | Daddy |

# WHAT CAN YOU SEE HERE?

dinosaur

monster

leaves

boy

knight

lizard

# POPPY IS RUDE!

Princess Poppy is having a bad day. When the king says she is far too little to ride on his great big horse, she pulls a silly face at him.

Then, when the queen says, 'Poppy! Don't be so rude!' she sticks her tongue out. So now she has been shut in the old tower until she learns to behave better.

Poppy stamps her foot. She shouts. She bangs on the door. And then she cries. She knows she has been naughty but it is so hard to be a good little princess all the time.

At last she curls up on the floor and falls asleep. She dreams that a knight rides up on a horse to rescue her.

53

They gallop away over hills full of flowers. Birds sing in the blue sky and Poppy is very, very happy.

When she wakes at last, her mother is there. 'Come on, Poppy,' she says, 'We know you are sorry now and the king has found a lovely small horse for you to ride.' Poppy beams.

So some of her dream will come true!

# KEY WORDS

| | |
|---|---|
| when | learns |
| of | mother |
| don't | know |
| come | found |
| good | small |
| horse | been |
| dream | birds |
| pulls | day |

# WHAT CAN YOU SEE HERE?

butterfly

flowers

candle

door

key

deer

# TWENTY APPLES

Rose and Alice are looking for their brothers. It is a lovely day. The sky is blue and birds are singing.

'Olly has gone to pick apples,' buzzes one little yellow bee. 'At the farm on the hill.'

'Billy has gone to pick apples, too,' says a red butterfly. 'On the hill by the sea.'

Off they run. They soon find
Billy on the hill by the sea.
There are ten apples on his tree.

'Take five,' says Billy. 'That is
half for you both, and half for
me. I want to stay and watch
the boats a little longer before
I come home.'

'Thank-you,' say Rose and
Alice. Then off they run to
find Olly.

They soon find Olly on the hill by the farm. There are ten apples on his tree, too.

'Take five,' says Olly. 'That is half for you two and half for me. I want to stay and watch the cows and sheep a little longer before I come home.'

'Thank-you,' say Rose and Alice. 'Now we all have five apples each. Aren't we lucky?'

# KEY WORDS

| | |
|---|---|
| birds | hill |
| day | looking |
| farm | says |
| sheep | has |
| soon | sky |
| before | little |
| all | longer |
| come | five |

# WHAT CAN YOU SEE HERE?

cow

lighthouse

apple

fountain

windmill

boat

# SAND, SEA AND CASTLES

Jane lives near the sea. She loves to swim every day. One day she sees her uncle, the king, paddling in the water.

'I wish I could swim like you, Jane,' says the king. 'Can you show me how? I'm a bit scared.'

Daddy smiles at his brother and says, 'I am sure Jane can help you, Joe!'

So Jane takes the king into the sea and shows him how to swim. It takes a few days but at last he manages to do it. The king is so pleased and happy. He shouts, 'Hooray. I can do it! At last!'

Then he sits in a deck chair and gives Daddy his spare crown to keep the sun off his head. Jane builds a sandcastle.

'Would you like to see a real castle,' asks King Joe. 'Would you like to see my castle, Jane? Your dad has been to stay but you never have.'

'Yes, please!' says Jane.

So the very next day they go for tea at the castle. King Joe gives Jane a beautiful dress and another of his spare crowns – to say thank-you for his excellent swimming lessons!

# KEY WORDS

| | |
|---|---|
| ask | the |
| chair | gives |
| sea | please |
| head | show |
| water | yes |
| how | you |
| I | last |
| every | and |

# WHAT CAN YOU SEE HERE?

carriage

crab

bucket

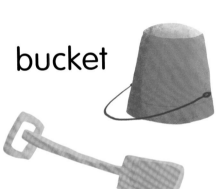

palm tree

spade

fish

castle

# TIMID TIM

There was once a very poor, very lonely, very hungry knight called Tim (short for timid because Tim was NOT brave!).

One day there was nothing left to eat except one egg. Tim boiled it for three minutes but when he sat down to eat, instead of a tasty yellow middle, he found a baby dragon inside!

The dragon huffed and puffed and began to grow. Soon she was HUGE. She took Timid Tim flying high to save maidens in distress. They saved lots of lovely girls and princesses. ALL of them wanted to marry Timid Tim.

'Oh dear. It is good to have so many friends now,' cried Tim. 'But I cannot marry everyone!'

'I have a good idea,' said the dragon. She took Tim to a prison where a witch was keeping boys and princes.

The dragon scared the witch away while Tim helped the boys to escape. Soon there were lots of weddings and the dragon was invited to them all. Tim married a sweet young princess and was never lonely, poor, hungry – or timid – again.

# KEY WORDS

| | |
|---|---|
| wanted | began |
| where | while |
| helped | never |
| because | lots |
| every | took |
| found | friend |
| good | cannot |
| bigger | dear |

# WHAT CAN YOU SEE HERE?

rabbit

dragon egg

dragon

plate

spider

rainbow

# WHEN I GROW UP

Leo, Lucy and Jack are good friends. They always sit next to each other at school.

One day the teacher asks, 'Now what would you like to do when you leave school?'

'I am going to be an astronaut,' shouts Leo, 'I shall fly in space, go to the Moon and see all the planets.'

'That is really exciting!' says Mrs. Brown.

'I love to dance,' says Lucy. 'So I shall be a ballerina and dance all day long and be on the stage.'

'So you might be a big star,' says Mrs. Brown, smiling.

'Watch out, Leo!' giggles Jack. 'She might be up in space, too – if she's a star.'

'Not that kind of star, silly!' says Lucy.

'I like insects and animals
and watching wild things,'
says Jack.
'I think I shall explore and go
to exciting places and see lions
and elephants and giant
spiders.'

'Wow!' says Mrs Brown,
'You must practice your writing
now so that one day you can
send each other letters about
all your adventures.'

# KEY WORDS

| | |
|---|---|
| like | school |
| teacher | that |
| doing | going |
| really | am |
| places | they |
| writing | long |
| would | must |
| say | things |

# WHAT CAN YOU SEE HERE?

doll

alien

dragonfly

planet

rocket

bird

# RAIN AND RAINBOWS

It is raining. It is raining hard. Drip, drip, drip. Iris and Dolly are sad. They want to go out. Teddy is cross.

'I don't like rain!' he says. 'And this is the wettest I have ever seen. Silly, dripping rain! Just when we want to go outside.'

Then the sun peeps out. And there by the window is a little man in green.

Outside is a rainbow. It is red and pink and blue and yellow.

'It is time to have some fun at the fair,' says the funny little man in the green hat.
'We just need to slide over the rainbow.'

'Stop! Wait for us!' shout Teddy and Dolly. But Iris has gone. She is sliding high, up and away.

Teddy waits by the window.
Dolly waits too.

Then, at last, they see Iris sliding
back down again.

Iris waves goodbye to the funny
little man. She gives Dolly a
big hug.

Then she gives Teddy
an even bigger hug.
'The fair was fun,'
says Iris.
'But it is even better
being home with my
two very best friends.'